Keyboard *from the* Beginning Songbook

by Christopher Hussey

Published by
Chester Music Limited

Exclusive Distributors:
Hal Leonard
7777 West Bluemound Road, Milwaukee, WI 53213
Email: info@halleonard.com

Hal Leonard Europe Limited
42 Wigmore Street, Marylebone, London WIU 2 RY
Email: info@halleonardeurope.com

Hal Leonard Australia Pty. Ltd.
4 Lentara Court, Cheltenham, Victoria 9132, Australia
Email: info@halleonard.com.au

The author and publisher would like to thank Martha Cowan, our
keyboard player model.

Diagrams by Richard Lemon at Fresh Lemon
Music processing and layout by Christopher Hussey
Edited by Toby Knowles

www.wisemusicclassical.com

Contents

Note for teachers

This songbook contains a selection of well-loved songs and classical favourites arranged for the beginner keyboard player.

Starting with very simple tunes for just one hand, and progressing to easily-mastered pieces for both hands, including chord and ostinato accompaniments, this structured collection will help build the student's technique, and at the same time, increase their repertoire.

Perfect as a complementary resource to use alongside the **Keyboard from the Beginning** tutor book (see page 32), this songbook provides additional material to support each stage of the course, offering reinforcement and further development of the skills learnt.

It is equally appropriate for those learning the keyboard or piano, and to support individual or class teaching.

Lyrics are included for most of the songs in the first part of this book to help the student with their rhythm as they progress towards playing with an independent right and left hand. Pointers are given to help, along with some ideas for further activities.

Playing the keyboard is enormously rewarding and students will have many hours of fun ahead of them as they learn how to play new repertoire.

Note Guide

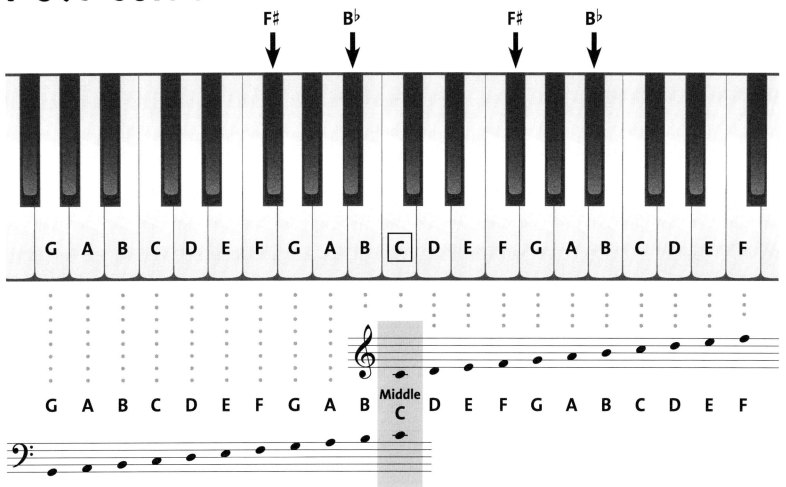

Flats and sharps

A **flat** sign ♭ lowers a note by one step (a **semitone**) to the very next key on the left.

A **sharp** sign ♯ raises a note by one step (a **semitone**) to the very next key on the right.

Jingle Bells

Words & Music by James Lord Pierpont

Position your right hand as shown:

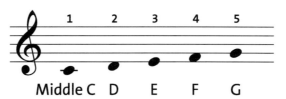

Middle C   D   E   F   G

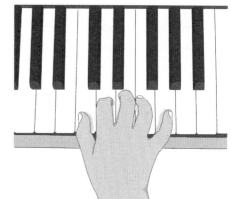

See page 16 for a version of this tune that uses both hands.

Jin - gle bells, jin - gle bells, jin - gle all the way.

Oh, what fun it is to ride in a one - horse o - pen sleigh, hey!

Jin - gle bells, jin - gle bells, jin - gle all the way.

Oh, what fun it is to ride in a one - horse o - pen sleigh.

When The Saints Go Marching In

Use the right-hand position shown opposite. Watch out for the **repeat sign** at the end.

See page 27 for a version of this tune with chords in your left hand as an accompaniment.

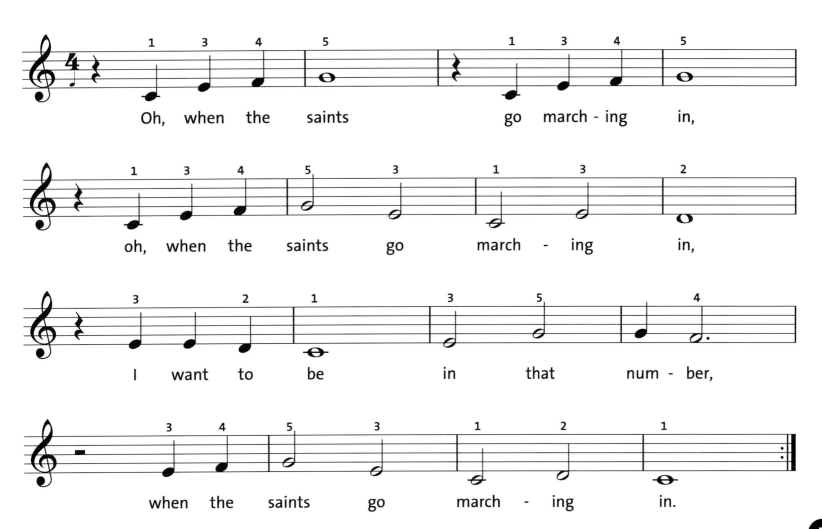

Lavender's Blue

Position your right hand as shown on page 6. Watch out for the shift of hand position as you stretch to reach the note A with your little finger (finger 5) at the point marked with an arrow. Your right hand returns to its starting position two bars later.

Lav - en - der's blue, dil - ly, dil - ly, lav - en - der's green;

when I am king, dil - ly, dil - ly, you shall be queen.

Skip To My Lou

Start with the right-hand position on page 6. In this song, your thumb (finger 1) stretches to reach the note B shown by the arrow.

Skip, skip, skip to my Lou, skip, skip, skip to my Lou,

skip, skip, skip to my Lou, skip to my Lou, my dar - lin'.

Dear Liza

Look at the fingering above the first note, F, and position your right hand so it's ready to begin. Your hand shifts position a few times in this song, shown by the arrows.

This song begins on the third beat of the bar—the **upbeat** (or **anacrusis**).

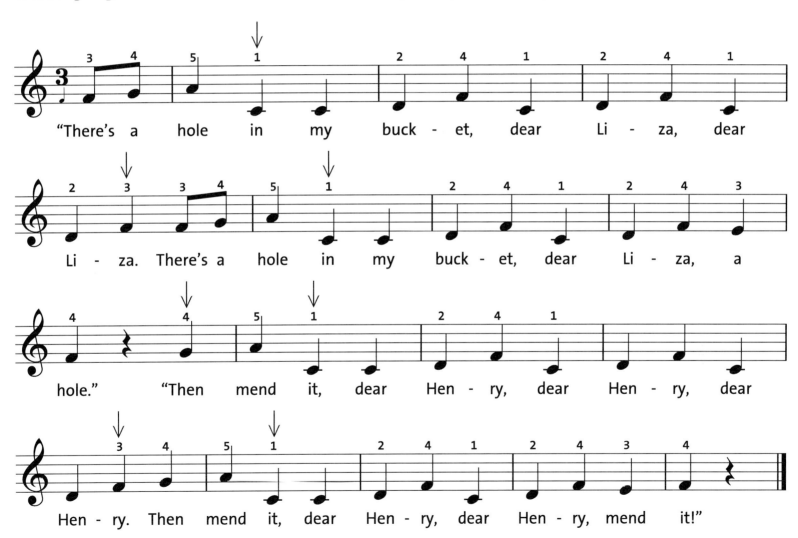

"There's a hole in my buck - et, dear Li - za, dear

Li - za. There's a hole in my buck - et, dear Li - za, a

hole." "Then mend it, dear Hen - ry, dear Hen - ry, dear

Hen - ry. Then mend it, dear Hen - ry, dear Hen - ry, mend it!"

Polly Wolly Doodle

Place the 2nd finger of your right hand on Middle C to prepare for this song and watch out for the arrows, which show a shift in hand position.

Oranges And Lemons

Position your right hand as shown.

Watch out for the shifts of hand position — the first at the start of the third line of music, and then back to this new position eight bars later.

F G A B♭ C

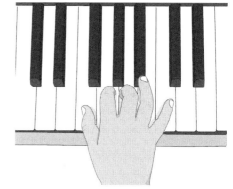

"Or - an - ges and lem - ons," say the bells of Saint Clem - ent's. "You

owe me five far - things," say the bells of Saint Mar - tin's.

"When will you pay me?" say the bells of Old Bai - ley. "When I grow

rich," say the bells of Shore - ditch. "When will that be?" say the

bells of Step - ney. "I do not know," says the great bell of Bow.

Little Playmates

Composed by Franz Xaver Chwatal

Position your left hand as shown:

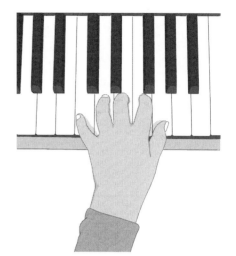

Watch out for the dots above or below some notes, which tell you to play them **staccato** — short and detached.

See page 26 for a version of this tune that uses both hands.

Long, Long Ago

Words & Music by Thomas Haynes Bayly

Position your left hand as shown opposite, ready to begin this song. Watch out for the two points where your 2nd finger crosses over your thumb and back again, marked with arrows.

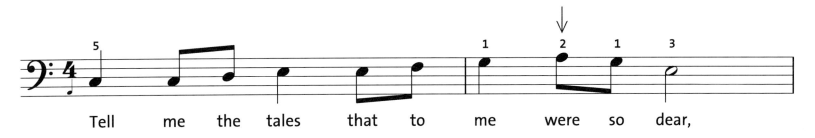

Tell me the tales that to me were so dear,

long, long a - go, long, long a - go. Sing me the songs I de -

- light - ed to hear, long, long a - go, long a - go.

Try playing this tune smoothly, in a **legato** style. Experiment with the different sounds on your keyboard and choose one that you think works well for this gentle song.

Largo ('From The New World')

Composed by Antonín Dvořák

In this piece, you will need both hands.

Position them on the notes as shown,
before you play.

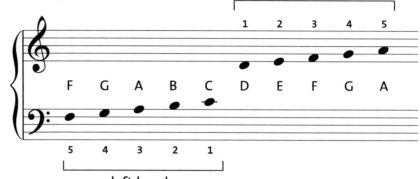

Sing A Lullaby

Position your hands on the notes as shown.

In this tune you will play with both hands at the same time. Your right hand and left hand play the same tune here, an octave apart.

> Your teacher could accompany you using the chord symbols.

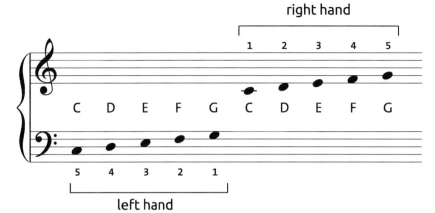

Jingle Bells

Words & Music by James Lord Pierpont

Place your right and left hands in the positions shown on page 15. Both hands are playing the tune here, an octave apart.

Your teacher could accompany you using the chord symbols.

Twinkle, Twinkle Little Star

Words by Jane Taylor, Music Traditional

Position your hands as shown on page 15. Your left hand stays in this position, but your right hand shifts position a number of times. Keep your eye on the fingering!

Take a look at the first line of music and the third line — what do you notice?

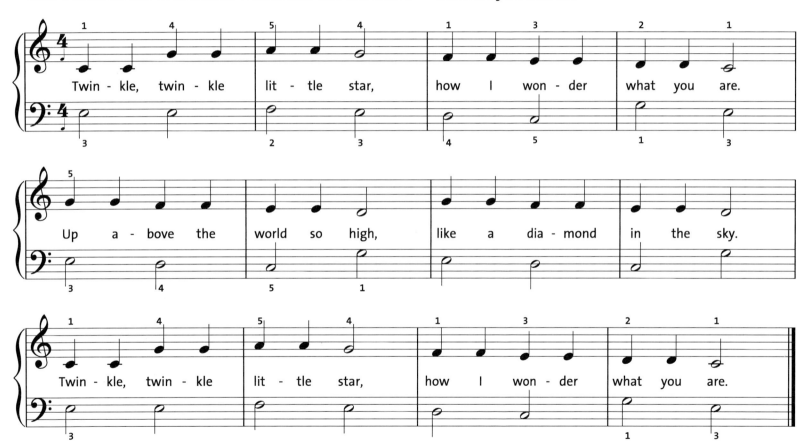

If your keyboard has a record function, you could record the left hand on its own, and then play it back, playing along with the right hand. You might also want to perform this song as a duet.

A-tisket, A-tasket

> ♪ This is a **quaver rest** — it tells you to be silent for a quaver (half a crotchet beat).

Your left hand stays in a fixed position, but your right hand moves in this tune. Practise hands separately first, before putting them together.

Old MacDonald Had A Farm

The tune in your right hand uses the **major pentatonic scale** in G — the five notes G, A, B, D and E.

Watch the fingering closely to help you with the changes of hand position, and look out for the ♯ (sharp) and ♭ (flat) signs in the left hand.

♮ is a **natural** sign, which tells you to cancel the effect of a flat or sharp sign.

Swing Low, Sweet Chariot

This tune in your right hand uses the **major pentatonic scale** in F—the five notes F, G, A, C and D.

Watch out for the **ties** in your right hand.

Go Tell It On The Mountain

The tune in your right hand uses the **major pentatonic scale** in G—the five notes G, A, B, D and E.

Keep an eye on the fingering in the right hand to help you shift hand position and play the tune more easily.

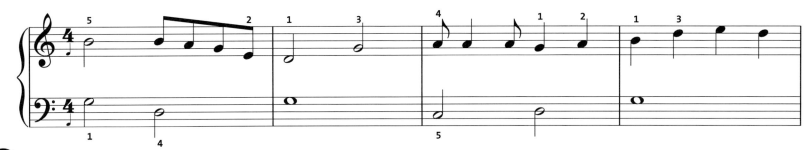

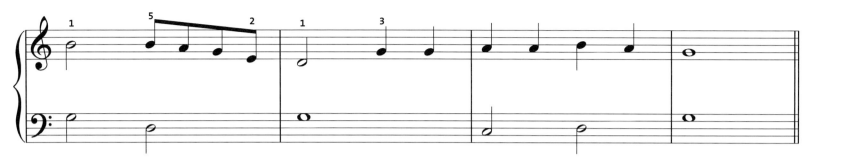

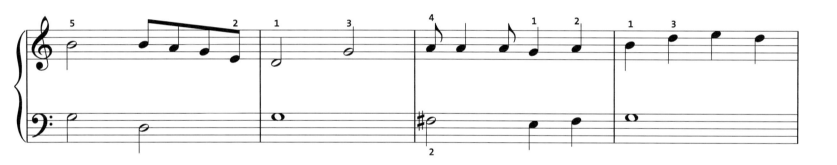

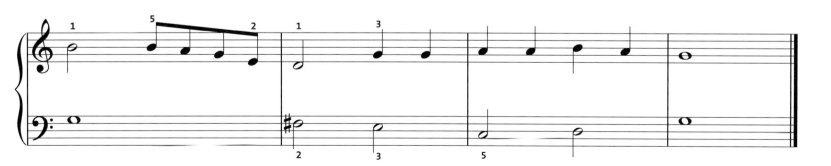

21

Oh! Susanna

Words & Music by Stephen Foster

Look at the notes used in the right-hand tune in the first eight bars, up to the repeat sign. How many different notes are used? Do you remember what we call this set of notes? (Look at **Swing Low, Sweet Chariot** on page 20).

Row, Row, Row Your Boat

Your left hand plays an **ostinato** accompaniment in this tune. This is the name given to a repeating phrase.

Class activity

Divide into two groups and try this as a **round**.

One group begins, and when they reach bar 5, the second group begins. Each group plays the tune through twice.

Scene From 'Swan Lake'

Composed by Pyotr Ilyich Tchaikovsky

Watch out for the sharps (♯) and flats (♭) used in this piece, and the **dynamic mark** *p* (**piano** = quiet).

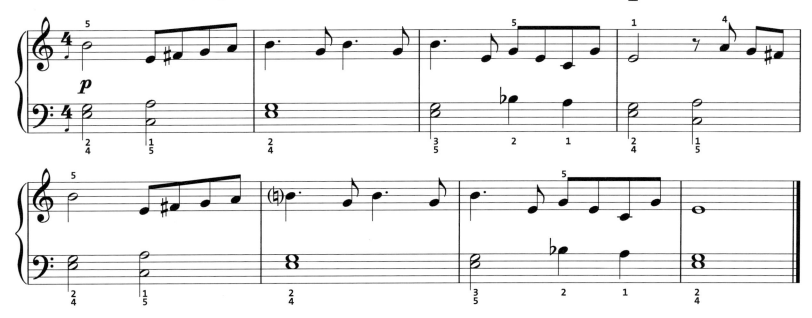

Bobby Shafto

Watch out for the **dynamic mark** *f* (**forte** = loud) at the start. Keep the left hand light when playing the **staccato** notes.

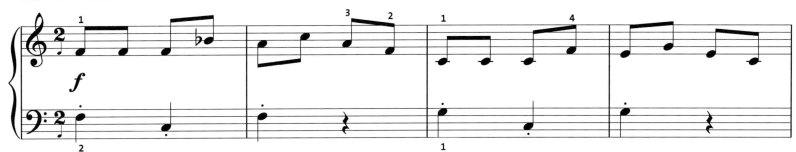

24

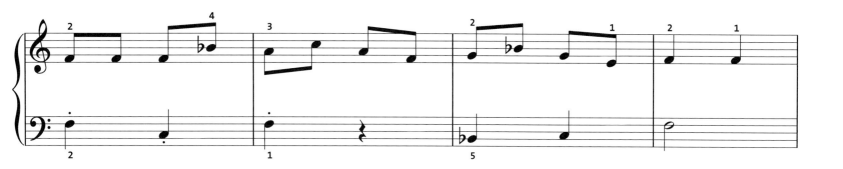

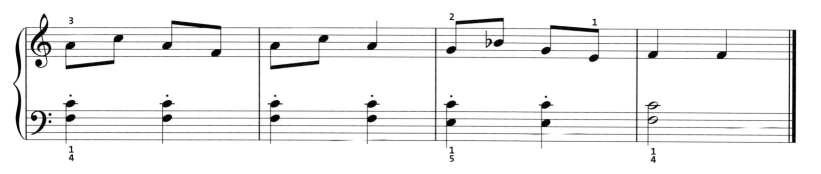

25

Little Playmates

Composed by Franz Xaver Chwatal

This piece uses the three-note **chords (triads)** of **C major** and **G major** to accompany the tune. You've already played this tune in your left hand on page 12.

The first phrase is played in your right hand with the chords in your left hand, and for the second phrase, the tune swaps to your left hand and the chords to your right hand. Keep the hand playing the chords quieter than the other so that the tune can sing out over the accompaniment.

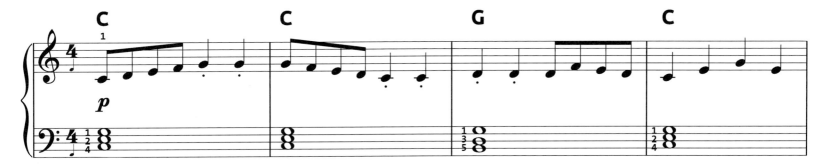

Experiment with the different sounds on your keyboard and choose one that you think works well for this chirpy song.

When The Saints Go Marching In

This song uses the left-hand chords of **C major**, **G major** and **F major** to accompany this familiar tune.

Now try the same right-hand tune with the left-hand part below, which uses the same chords, but this time you play the notes of each chord in sequence, as a **broken chord**.

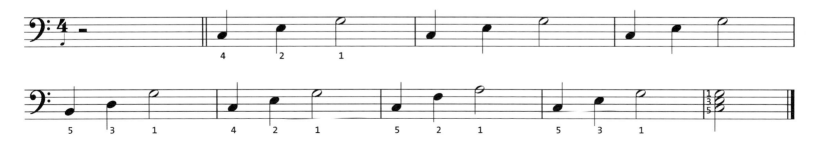

Silent Night

Words by Joseph Mohr, Music by Franz Xaver Gruber

Can you work out the name of the broken chords you are playing in your left hand? (Have a look at page 27.)

Michael, Row The Boat Ashore

What Shall We Do With The Drunken Sailor?

Try playing the right-hand tune with **staccato** notes as if dots had been written below or above each note.

Spring (from 'The Four Seasons')

Composed by Antonio Vivaldi

Keyboard *from the* Beginning

The **Keyboard From The Beginning** tutor book is an enjoyable and accessible introduction to playing the keyboard, which requires no previous experience of playing an instrument or of reading music.

It provides a straightforward teaching scheme, ideal for 6–12 year-olds, through a selection of exciting original tunes and well-loved favourites, and will get you making music right from your first lesson. The book and audio edition is accompanied by downloadable audio tracks, providing fun and inspiring accompaniments for you to play along with while you are practising or performing.

Book only
CH83160

Book + Audio
CH83204